FRAGMENTS OF MINE & MILL IN WALES

FRAGMENTS OF MINE & MILL IN WALES

ALUN JOHN RICHARDS

ISBN: 0-86381-812-9

Cover design: Sian Parri

First published in 2002 by
Gwasg Carreg Gwalch, 12 Iard yr Orsaf, Llanrwst, Wales LL26 0EH
01492 642031 01492 641502
books@carreg-gwalch.co.uk Internet: www.carreg-gwalch.co.uk

Front cover:
Crusher frame Cwm Cowarch lead mine; Crusher roll Cwm Cowarch lead mine;
Ffestiniog Railway train passes in front of Cwmorthin slate tips at Tanygrisiau;
Pelena viaduct; Ynyspandy slate mill.
Back cover:
Y Moelwyn; Blondin Tower, Penrhyn quarry; Pulley, Penyrorsedd quarry;
Ffestiniog Railway c1870.

Printed in Malta by Interprint Limited

Dedicated to the late Dr. G. A. (Tony) Rawlins. DSC. FRCA
His words encouraged, his friendship enriched

Acknowledging the help and assistance of amongst many, Griff R. Jones & Richard M. Williams

INTRODUCTION

Over forty years of travelling around Wales by train, car, motorcycle and aeroplane have afforded me many opportunities to take photographs. Most of those opportunities, I have missed. So much that seemed ordinary proved to be extraordinary – after it had vanished. So many things left 'until next time', were not there the next time.

I make no apology for this collection being so slate orientated, since slate workings leave such a proud and almost indelible stamp on the hillsides. Indeed the twin walls of a roofless drum house standing stark against a skyline provide a more evocative emblem of Wales than leek or daffodil. Furthermore although Welsh slate no longer roofs the world, its prestige as the ultimate material is undiminished.

I have endeavoured to make some record of what has gone, what is going and what is just plain peculiar.

Alun John Richards 2002

THE AUTHOR

Alun John Richards is a retired engineer who was for many years a Guest Tutor at the Snowdonia National Park Environmental Study Centre, Plas Tan y Bwlch and a sometime lecturer at Coleg Harlech Summer Schools.

A native of Swansea, he is a past Chairman of the South West Wales Industrial Archaeology Society and writes and lectures on the Welsh Slate and Metal Mining Industries.

By the same author

A Gazeteer of the Welsh Slate Industry	IBSN 0-86381-196-5
Slate Quarrying at Corris	IBSN 0-86381-279-1
Slate Quarrying in Wales	IBSN 0-86381-319-4
Slate Quarrying in Pembrokeshire	IBSN 0-86381-484-0
The Slate Regions of North & Mid Wales	IBSN 0-86381-552-9
The Slate Railways of Wales	IBSN 0-86381-689-4

CONTENTS

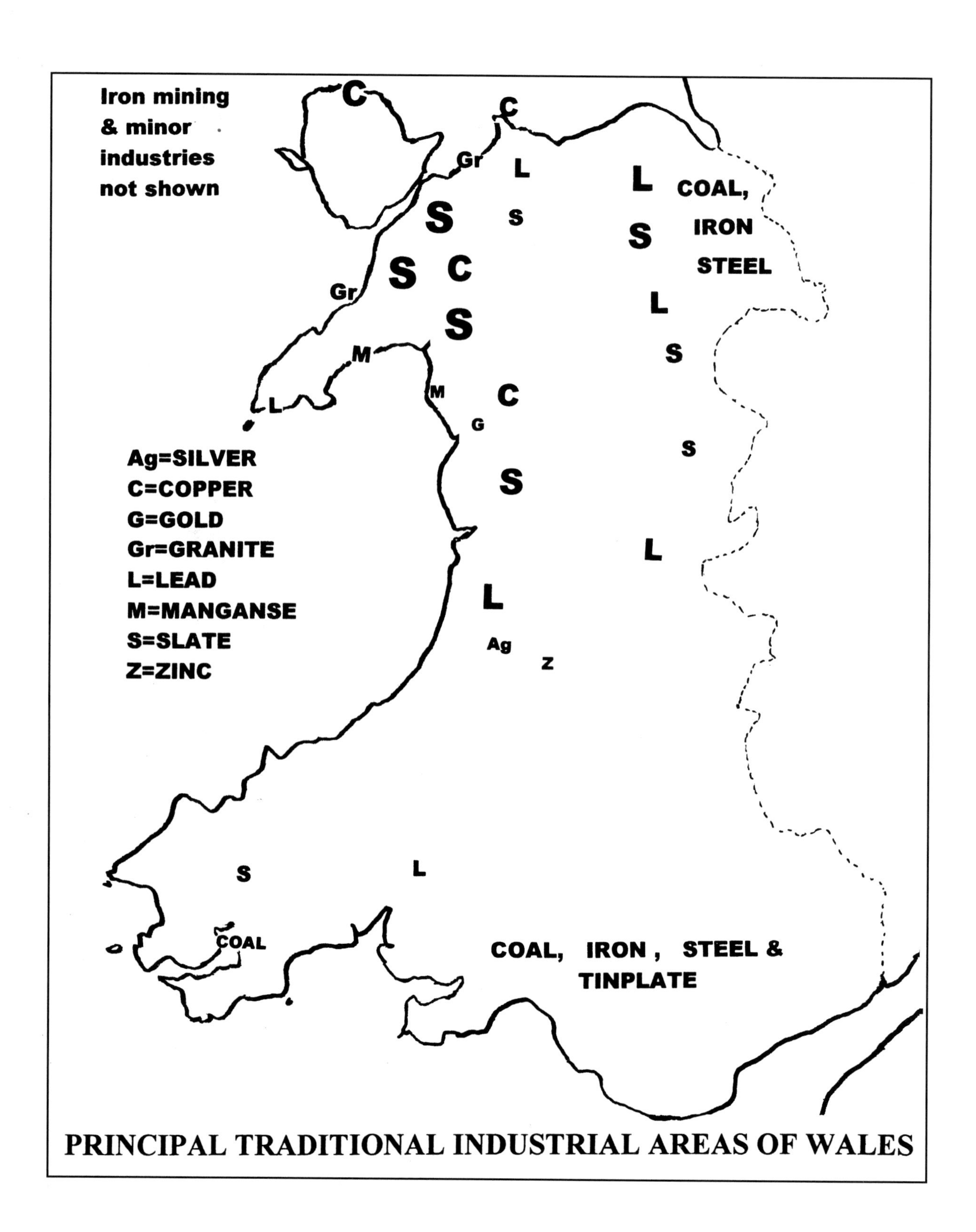

PRINCIPAL TRADITIONAL INDUSTRIAL AREAS OF WALES

FRAGMENTS OF MINE & MILL IN WALES

Time has moved on, the heavy and extractive industries of Wales, some whose history spans centuries, others that must be chronicled in millennia, have all but vanished. The world no longer depends on Welsh iron, steel, tin plate, coal and copper, nor even that Welshest of products, slate.

Of the extractive activities, some coal and some slate survives but totally shunned are the harvests of the meinars who eviscerated mountains in their insatiable search for gold and silver, lead and copper, iron and zinc, manganese and almost every kind of metal, mineral and even stone.

The captains, the adventurers, the speculators, have all passed on, enriched, or more likely pauperized by the seductive strumpets of vein and lode. So too have the men, and their loyal wives, who sacrificed life and health and limb wresting a pittance from the reluctant rock.

Now adits have collapsed, roofless mills lie stripped of machines. Woodwork has rotted or served to warm a passing traveller. Iron rusts, structures crumble, walls lean and pillars teeter in balletic postures.

Choked and overgrown, their tracks ripped up, their formations sinking, are tramways and railways which once sped the slates and ores to the coast. The docks and wharves from where locally built and locally manned ships sailed literally to the ends of the earth, are now derelict.

Communities struggle to find new reasons to exist. On the hillsides trees and nettles grow among stones, once the pridefully spotless homes of men and women who lived and loved, raised families and passed on to chapel graveyards. Graveyards whose memorials to deacons and poets totter and decay as tightly in the brambles' grip as those of rakes and tosspots.

All these and the detritus that accompanied almost every extractive activity serve to recall a proud heritage. Each day these relics shrink and diminish. Each day battles are lost against the elements, vandals, developers, thieves, landscaping bulldozers and the effluxion of time.

Much of what I have recorded over the latter third of the twentieth century has now gone; much more will go. At some time we shall be left with scant tangible vestige of industries, which supplied the world with their goods and a way of life, which supplied the world with their example.

AJR

TRANSPORT

Man hauled barges on the river Teifi at Cilgerran, northern Pembrokeshire c1820 (SN196429)

Although transport has no end product, without it there is no trade, no commerce no industry. Nothing is made, nothing is sold, no livelihoods are provided, no wealth is created. Products cannot be moved to market and supplies cannot be brought to any enterprise or its workforce.

Pont y Porthmon, early drovers bridge (SH802399)

Without transport people and communities could only survive by exploiting the plants, the animals, the stones or whatever presented itself in their immediate locality. Their existence would differ little from that of the Stone Age.

When roads were almost non-existent, the basic transport was coastwise shipping. Wooden sailing vessels were built and crewed at dozens of creeks around the coast of Wales, where trading and fishing communities grew up. In the inland areas, people subsistence farmed in a barter economy.

Despite this there was much industry in Wales. Copper mining and smelting dates from the Bronze Age, slate probably not much later. Iron working long predated the Romans. During the Middle Ages coal was raised on a commercial scale and mining for lead and silver became widespread. By the 18th century Wales or at least parts of it, could be described as 'industrialized'.

Road made by Graig Ddu slate quarry in 1803 (SH719440)

Cemlyn quay, 18th century shipping point on the river Dwyryd (SH660402)

Smelting and manufacture were, as far as possible, carried out close to water since a stream could provide power and a river, or the sea itself could offer transport. Coal sometimes outcropped on the shore, but minerals were generally not so obliging, so output had to be laboriously carried on packhorses or mules or even on men's backs.

River transport generally involved some mixture of rowing, sailing, poling, or more often than not, man hauling. In the late 18th and early 19th centuries canals were built which well served the south Wales valleys but were of scant use to the sparse mountainous areas of the rest of

Wales.

To escape the use of expensive and inefficient pack animals, some metal mine and big slate quarry owners, built roads to a river or to the coast.

A number of the minor roads in both Gwynedd and northern Ceredigion owe their origin to early industrial transport needs.

Various industrialists built river quays or seaports, some of the latter, for better or worse surviving as marinas.

Roads could only be of limited use, carting a dozen miles could easily double the cost of a mineral product. Weather could halt all movement in winter and the need for horses and men to bring in the harvest could bring matters to a standstill in summer.

Metal mining, being then generally on a small scale and with a comparatively expensive end product, could cope with the vicissitudes of cartage, coal could not. A wooden wagon way was put in by Sir Humphrey Mackworth to carry the output of his collieries to the river Neath. In the late 17th century and during the 18th century an increasing number of wagon ways and tramways were in use in the coalfields.

Penrhyn Railroad Marchogion Drum house and stables (SH548679)

Green road defines route of Dinorwig Tramway (SH578625)

By the late 18th century the slate quarries were expanding but the increased costs of horses and fodder due to the French wars, was exacerbating transport problems.

This caused Lord Penrhyn, the largest slate producer, to lay down the Penrhyn Railroad in 1801 to carry the output of his quarries to his dock at Port Penrhyn near Bangor. It was of course horse drawn but made much more efficient use of the then scarce animals. It became the prototype for more than a score of narrow gauge lines, some of which still operate as the 'Great Little Trains of Wales'.

Sleeper blocks Nantlle Railway (SH503533)

The Penrhyn Railroad lasted in its original form until 1876, thus a line designed in the 18th century survived almost until the 20th.and much of its route is traceable in the 21st. Such longevity did not attend the next line, the Dinorwig Tramway, opened in 1824 it mirrored the Penrhyn line in carrying slate from a quarry (Dinorwig) to a port (Port Dinorwig), but it lasted a bare nineteen years, although some of its route and formations do remain.

The third line, the Nantlle Railway of 1828 was a public railway, not the first in Wales, which was the Carmarthenshire Railway of 1802, but certainly the first in north Wales. Run like a turnpike road, users provided their own wagons and horses.

Nantlle Railway bridge, over afon Gwyrfai (SH478500)

Bont Fawr carried tracks over the Nantlle Tramway (SH495533)

It enabled the various slate quarry owners in Nantlle Vale to reach the port of Caernarfon, avoiding the onerous turnpike tolls. Although largely superceded by the standard gauge railway from the 1870s, the final section remained in use, still horse drawn, until 1963.

Chronologically the next rail line was the Ffestiniog Railway of 1836. By far the most important of any slate line it had particularly after its 1863 steaming, worldwide technical influence. Happily it is still with us.

The Padarn Railway replaced the Dinorwig Tramway in 1842, and 6 years later it was amongst the very first lines in Wales to use steam. Designed for locomotive use, it avoided intermediate inclines, running from the base of Dinorwig quarry to a point above Port Dinorwig.

A gauge of 2' had become established in the quarry but locomotives of such a small size were unavailable Thus a gauge of 4' was adopted, the quarry gauge wagons being carried on transporter trucks. These were unloaded at the port terminus and lowered down to the dockside on an incline

It is remarkable that this somewhat ramshackle arrangement continued in use until the 1960s.

Its route alongside the lake has been re-used by the Padarn Lake Railway employing mostly ex-quarry locomotives. The rest of the route, though not continuously open, is traceable as far as the great Penscoins drum house cum transfer depot. This unique structure disappeared in the 1990s in a signal act of official vandalism. Fortunately the adjacent engine sheds etc still remain.

Besides the 'famous' lines like these and the Tal-y-llyn and the Corris, there were many other more modest rail links, such as the magnificently unsuccessful Gorseddau, which opened with great pomp and ceremony in

Southern end of Moelwyn tunnel Ffestiniog Railway (SH679428)

Southern end of Garnedd tunnel FR (SH658413)

Footbridge at Bethel, Padarn Railway (SH529653)

1856. The Gorseddau was saved from oblivion by being extended and re-gauged in 1875. On the strength of a solitary De Winton locomotive, it called itself a steam railway but within little more than a decade solitary trucks were being trundled by hand to Porthmadog. Its lower end was successfully re-utilized by the Moel y Gest tramway during the early 1900s. Some of the formations are traceable and its route, still defines streets in Porthmadog. It was the only line of its kind in the area never to have inclines. Equally modest was the 1864 Croesor tramway, whose last few miles served the Welsh Highland Railway and at the time of writing appears destined to do so again. The upper part in Cwm Croesor, with its three notable clapper bridges, served farmers long after the 1930s closure and now makes a fine footpath. Legend has it that housewives pushed trucks along the lower part to bring shopping home from Porthmadog.

Penscoins drum house, Padarn railway (SH532678)

Croesor Tramway bridge (SH631447)

There were many other even less well-known rail links, particularly in that great decade of rail laying, the 1860s. The Rhiw-bach tramway which linked hitherto inaccessible workings to the Ffestiniog Railway and whose inclines raised groceries and commuting schoolmistresses to the remote and loftily sited quarry settlement, and the

Aberllefeni Tramway (SH770202)

Cedryn Tramway (SH742662)

Graig Ddu down whose inclines the teachers returned. home on 'Wild Cars'. The R'alltgoed tramway, a Corris Railway feeder, whose trucks conveyed the devout to chapel and another Corris line the short Aberllefenni branch which in the 1970s was the last surviving horse-drawn slate railway (although by this time tractor pulled).

There was the Cedryn tramway, which fruitlessly drove deep into the Snowdonia fastnesses, in the expectation of bringing slate to the river Conwy.

In the 1870s the tramway building continued. The heroic inclines of the Hafod y Llan line tumbling hundreds of meters down the Snowdon flank, in frantic haste to meet a railway, which was never built.

The quite extraordinary Deeside tramway whose anachronistic wooden rails seemed to reach back into the past, towards the epic days of Owain Glyndŵr, at whose Glyndyfrdwy birthplace it terminated.

The clanking, rickety Hendre Ddu Tramway which in addition to carrying slate in times of peace and timber in times of war, provided the sole communication along the secret, hidden valley of the river Angell, a distant tributary of the Dyfi. Whilst it could not match the door-to-door capability of the

Wooden rails Deeside tramway (SJ145410)

Village branch of the Tal-y-llyn Railway which served almost every house in Abergynolwyn, nevertheless several farms had private branches. There was also the Glyn Valley Tramroad, a strange amalgam of street tramway and industrial railway, carrying slate and granite and all manner of things. Sponsored by the mighty London & North Western Railway, at one time the largest Limited Company in the world, it sought to do the proud and haughty Great Western Railway in the eye, by connecting with the Montgomeryshire canal. Unfortunately commercial pressures demanded rail connection and the L&NWR had to allow an interchange with the rival line.

Revised course of Hendre Ddu tramway at Aberangell (SH842103)

The final flourish of the slate railways of Wales was the North Wales Narrow Gauge. Opened in 1877 the year the slate market collapsed. Had the Light Railways Act been in force enabling cheaper construction, it might have stood a chance. As it was, even the much attenuated plan that was actually built, was a commercial disaster. In 1923, it reopened in extended form as the Welsh Highland Railway. Since this

Cwmsymlog lead mine tramway (SN698837)

Level crossing Fron sub-branch, North Wales Narrow Gauge Railway (SH507549)

Foel Ispri gold mine tramway (SH706200)

was the year the post-war slate boom came to an end, this re-incarnation proved even more fiscally unfortunate.

Following almost twenty years of brave efforts by the Welsh Highland revivivalists, with track re-laid on the formation of a standard gauge siding; the complete rebuilding of the WHR began in 2000. By utilising the trackbed of the old Caernarfon Afon-wen branch the new line will run from Caernarfon (where the original line ought to have started).

Not all the tramways of northern Wales were for slate. There were the magnificently robust inclines that lowered granite road stone and setts to the sea between Conwy and Bangor, and on the northern coast of Llŷn.

As far as metal mines were concerned, few had outputs sufficiently large to justify the expense of rails other than the big lead mines at Minera and the Van mines which had standard gauge branches. Other lead workings had internal tramways. One of the longest was the half-mile of line at Bryndyfi (SN683934) that joined the almost totally barren adit to the elaborate but unused crusher house.

Much more profitable was the big Cwmsymlog mining complex, the formations of whose internal tramways along

Glyncorrwg Mineral Railway (SS790981)

Pelena Viaduct GMR (SS810962)

Nant Llynfell incline (SN763161)

with much other remains still survive.

For gold mines, or at any rate Welsh gold mines, carrying away their product was more a matter of a haversack or even a pocket rather than wagons railed or otherwise. However since 1oz per ton was a most satisfactory yield, there was an awful lot of ore to be moved as well as development rock, so all but the very smallest mine would have rails of some kind to dump the dead rock and to bring the ore to where it was to be crushed and separated.

More spectacular than most was the tramway high above Bont Ddu which linked several associated workings. Its track bed makes a splendid walk.

As far as coal mining is concerned, there tend to be few tramroad relics of consequence since most were incorporated into standard gauge lines, although the routes of some are denoted by footpaths and lanes.

One of the more ambitious lines was the highly unsuccessful Glyncorrwg Mineral Railway which sought to connect coal workings in several south Wales valleys with the Neath canal. Since this involved crossing the grain of the country, serious engineering was called for. It had three inclines, one steam hauled, a deep cutting and a fine viaduct, which due to ground settlement had to be destroyed in the 1980s.

Manchester to Milford Railway (SN932800)

Apart from the railways and canals to carry coal and iron to markets, transport was required for the vast quantities of fluxing limestone needed for iron making. Thus for instance, the 19th century ironworks of Glamorganshire and Monmouth had horse tramways, which brought stone from the limestone belt to their immediate north. Many of these are still extant, the most notable fluxing stone transport relic is the comparatively modern (20th century) Nant Llynfell incline which brought limestone from the Black Mountains of Breconshire almost 1000'.

Usually a with-load descent incline would be self-acting, the weight of the down going loaded trucks serving to raise empty ones. The Nant Llynfell being over a mile and a quarter long this would be impracticable since the sheer weight of rope would stall the whole thing. Consequently a steam engine was required to move almost 5 tons of wire rope. The formation is visible for miles.

Not all tramway and railway lines were completed and the country abounds with formations, earthworks and cuttings that were commenced before finance was secured or legalities completed. One of the most notable was the Manchester and Milford Railway, which was to run southwest from a junction on the Mid Wales Railway just south of Llanidloes. The attempt to cut a tunnel that would have taken it out of the Wye valley, having failed, it came to a grinding halt just west of Llangurig. It carried one solitary contractor's train before abandonment. Some of the once-used formations and bridges remain. As soon as it was realized that the tunnel would never be cut, the line being built north from Carmarthen to meet it, was diverted to Aberystwyth, remaining in use for a century, as a valuable and now much missed link.

The Cribarth Mountain at the head of the Swansea valley was intensively exploited for limestone (for iron smelting flux and for agriculture) and rottenstone, (used for polishing tin plate) from around the 1820s. This has left the hillside scarred by the formations of the maze of tramways, which carried the stone to the Swansea canal.

Not all of the projected works were completed. On one flank of the mountain unused stone sleeper blocks, laboriously hauled up from the valley below, have lain for almost two centuries piled at measured intervals, marking the intended route of a never-built tramway.

Cribarth unused sleeper blocks (cSN838151)

SLATE QUARRIES

Slate quarrying was far from being the biggest Welsh industry, coal mining employed up to twenty times as many. Port Talbot steel works' payroll once exceeded the peak figure of the entire slate industry. Tinplate employed more, the railways employed more but slate was the one truly native industry. It functioned in the Welsh language using methods developed within Wales. It has also left the richest archaeological legacy.

A coal mine that has served its time is grassed over. A metal mine leaves maybe a hole and some tailings. A steelworks site is built over. A stone quarry reverts to nature. But a slate working leaves a wealth of relics and great heaps of waste that memorialise as permanently as any Egyptian pyramid or Greek temple. However much the sites are

Terracing at Penrhyn slate quarry, Bethesda. Sheds for a locomotive are on each level. (SH620650)

Penrhyn quarry bell-frame, (in top of previous picture)

landscaped, prettified, redeveloped or plundered for hardcore, they seem to defy all attempts to erase them.

Nevertheless time, the elements, gravity and vandalism whether criminal, commercial or corporate, do erode and diminish this inheritance. Also, for better reasons, relics of the past are of necessity being lost by continuing activity.

This is the situation at Penrhyn quarry which dominates the scene as it has done for more than two centuries, where, although some items such as their water balances have been preserved, current work is absorbing old relics at an ever increasing rate.

Not all slate workings were as successful as Penrhyn,

although the failure of Gorseddau quarry to produce more than a token tonnage has left a wealth of relicts unsullied by production.

Gorseddau's neighbour, Prince of Wales, also presents us with similarly almost pristine remains.

Gorseddau Slate Quarry, Cwm Pennant north of Porthmadog (SH573453)

Overhanging wall at Gorseddau, the purpose of which is disputed.

It stands with Gorseddau as a triumph of optimism over realism, each having swallowed millions in today's values, including the laying, relaying and extension of the Gorseddau tramway, for but trifling return.

In fact everything connected with that tramway seemed to turn to dust, a further extension was made to serve a notably non-productive copper mine.

Cutting on tramway extension at Prince of Wales

Prince of Wales Slate Quarry Cwm Pennant (SH549498)

Less profligate but again showing scant return was Arthog, a moderately successful operation, whose heavy early 1860s investments included a fine new incline to take advantage of the then new railway. It closed shortly afterwards.

Not all Welsh slate was quarried in the northern areas;

Pembrokeshire workings though ultimately dwarfed by the north's tonnages, produced up to the latter part of the 18th century, a substantial proportion of the Welsh total.

Since capital to build roads or railways was limited, the more successful workings tended to be on the coast where they could conveniently load into boats.

One of the most notable was Porth-gain, a self-contained community whose port, apart from shipping out slate, provided a gateway for a wide hinterland. When the slate ran out it diversified into brick making and roadstone quarrying.

Associated with Porth-gain and connected to it by a tramway was the neighbouring Abereiddi quarry. Their post-slate diversification was to have been a harbour to supplement Porth-gain. Since the quarry floor was below sea level, a channel was blasted to form an entrance, but the scheme was never completed.

One of the more unusual quarries is at Aberllefenni. After some early open digging it was developed by driving tunnels through the Foel Grochan Mountain and working the narrow, near vertical vein downwards in a manner unique to the area. Still very much in business extraction is now well below valley floor level.

Maenofferen at Blaenau Ffestiniog having closed in the late 1990s, Aberllefenni is now the only slate quarry to operate underground. Elsewhere untopping and open casting have now replaced the extraction of slate from chambers underground, so successfully developed at Blaenau Ffestiniog, to cope with the steeply dipping veins.

The most obvious relics in any slate quarry are the mills. Originally all work was done by hand, but from the early 19th century to speed the production of slabs for sills, gravestones, billiards tables, flooring and so on, saws were installed. By mid century, all but the very smallest unit had at least one powered

Arthog Slate Quarry near Fairbourne (SH650151)

Porth-gain, western Pembrokeshire. The quarry is top right. The slate was behind the then roofless warehouse; the bunkers are for the later roadstone works (SM813325)

Abereiddi Quarry 2 mile west of Porth-gain (SM795315)

Aberllefenni slate quarry, north of Machynlleth. It is possible to discern the 8 levels and the big 'Alma' cavern worked during the 1860s, before working went underground. (SH768103)

View from Cooke's Level Maenofferen, slate quarry Blaenau Ffestiniog so called because it was cut by a Cooke boring machine. This level, which latterly provided emergency access to the workings, was exposed during untopping of Bowydd chambers. Further untopping has now removed it (SH711462)

saw. These 'Machine Houses' or 'Engine Houses' came to be called mills, particularly after mechanical dressers and planers began to be used. A development which culminated in the big integrated mills of Blaenau Ffestiniog where all processes were concentrated under one roof

Some mills were modest, little more than huts, but some were quite elegant structures, the little mill at Prince of Wales, in spite of its remote location was designed to be something more than just a functional shed. Others were vast, containing dozens of saws and perhaps a similar number of dressing machines.

However for style and grace none matched the Ynys-y-pandy mill of the Gorseddau quarry. This extraordinary structure has been called the 'Cathedral of Welsh Slate'. In view of its total commercial failure; 'Mausoleum' might be a more appropriate sobriquet. Erected where ground could be had for the taking and intended to handle heavy block using

Cefn slate mill at Cligerran, north Pembrokeshire, in reuse (SN207229)

Understated elegance, the mill at Prince of Wales slate quarry (SH547494)

substantial machines, it is a mystery why it should depart from the universal single storey layout. It had two floors (four if one includes the basement workshop and attic store).

Water powered mills had to be located near a stream, which like Ynys-y-pandy could mean that they were a considerable distance from the quarry itself. When steam and more particularly electricity became available, mills could be sited anywhere, such as the 36 machine Australia mill at Dinorwig. Its remoteness, high up on

Ynys-y-pandy mill and tramway Cwm Pennant (SH550433)

Ynys-y-pandy mill

private ground has helped to ensure the survival of its saws although the building is now ruinous. A complete set of patterns for replicating these machines, including the Ingersoll nameplate exists at the Museum of Welsh Slate, so one wonders are they all

Australia mill, Dinorwig quarry, Llanberis (SH600602)

Messrs. Ingersoll's products?

Slate machinery makes good scrap, and likewise their buildings, whose location and layout may mean they are worth more as slates, trusses and block than as buildings. Even where work continues, old mill structures are replaced by ones better suited to modern methods.

Floor 5 Mill at Llechwedd was conveniently situated at the head of the big incline. When untopping replaced underground working, its position was no longer suitable and it was dismantled and replaced by a new building on a new site.

Although many mills have been taken (or allowed to fall) down, re-use has been found for some. This one at Clwt-y-bont (actually a writing slate factory on the original line of the Dinorwig Railway) has been re-used as a factory and depot.

Mill at Penrhyn quarry (SH620683)

Old and the new at Llechwedd Quarry, Blaenau Ffestiniog. Floor 5 Mill c1975, just before fork trucks took over entirely from the railed handling of blocks. (SH703467)

Mills were only one of the many buildings associated with a big slate quarry and even a small one would require a Powder House. This needed to be a secure building floored and if possible lined, against damp, ideally with strong walls and a frail roof to direct any explosion upwards. The basic structure was commonly circular but they varied widely in shape and complexity.

None were more elaborate than the fine powder store at Cwmorthin quarry. A huge blast wall surrounded its massive walls. Built in the early 1900s for a development that did not take place, it was quarried away in the 1990s, unused.

Smaller but notable for its wooden lining being almost intact is the magazine at the little Morben quarry near Machynlleth.

The square, lined powder house at Bwlch y Slaters survives, but many in the Blaenau Ffestiniog area were circular, sunk partly or wholly underground, the base of one is to be found at Blaen y Cwm quarry and until recently there was another at Oakeley.

At the tiny and remote Cae'r Gors quarry a miniature version of an underground powder house survives intact. The chamber is 8' diameter with 6' headroom and is approached by 18' wide steps and a passage some 10' long. The only other known (rather larger) example recently extant is near Graig Ddu quarry, which possibly dates from the earliest Manod workings of the 1800s.

More widespread than any other slate quarrying structures are the dressing sheds. It would be a very sorry little working indeed that did not have some shelter for splitting and dressing slates. At its most basic this might be just a wall, which could be crouched behind on one side or the other according to the wind direction. In fact the Welsh term Gwal literally means wall. However, normally there would be three walls and a back-sloping roof. It is rare indeed to find one with the roof intact,

Ex writing slate factory Clwt-y-bont near Llanberis (SH571630)

'Wendy House' Powder House at Hafodlas quarry, Betws-y-coed (SH779562)

'Beau Geste' Powder House Cwmorthin quarry Blaenau Ffestiniog (SH681462)

partly because the timbers would have rotted and partly because they were often made of nice handy, re-usable slabs!

Very small quarries would just have the one

Morben Quarry Powder House south west of Machynlleth (SN716993)

Morben

Remains of a Powder store Oakeley quarry Blaenau Ffestiniog (SH691471)

Cae'r Gors Powder store, Beddgelert in foreground slabs cover the entrance steps; the centre of the vaulted roof is missing. The figure is standing on debris (SH599514)

shelter, which probably doubled as store, mess-room and office.

Larger quarries might have rakes of three or four units, and in the very largest there would be dozens in rank after rank, particularly in the Caernarfonshire area where slate making within the mills was less common since the harder Cambrian rock does not machine trim well.

Sometimes they were in back-to-back rows, small ones on one side, for roofing slate and larger ones on the other for slabs. Occasionally there would be equal-sized pairs set back to back, which gave a choice of escaping the wind or driving rain. In the granite quarries stone setts were made in larger and more substantial sheds.

Minimalist shelter, Boundary Quarry on shore of Llyn Padarn (SH574613)

Quarrying demands bridges to cross external features and internal obstructions and to provide access within the quarries. One of the more prominent quarry bridges was the one which carried trucks emerging from 5 Level adit at Braich Goch quarry, Corris, across the then A470 to the head of a short incline which

Set making shelters Trefor granite quarry northern coast Llŷn peninsular (SH362460)

lowered them to mill level. Although rendered redundant in the 1950s when an internal incline enabled all material to emerge under the road from 6 Level adit. (Now the King Arthur's Caverns) The bridge survived for more than 20 years until the new road was built.

With iron, steel or timber costly, the short span bridges within workings were usually of slate slab, possibly with the abutments corbelled out to minimise the span. Some were relatively elaborate but many were very exiguous and it is surprising that they were able to carry the weight of loaded trucks of a ton or two, particularly as unsprung rolling stock on uneven track would induce big dynamic loadings.

Where due to the jointing of the rock precluded the production of long

Level 5 bridge Braich Goch Slate quarry, Corris (SH748079)

Minimalist bridge on the Gorseddau Railway extension, which allegedly carried a locomotive. Cwm Pennant (SH545490)

slabs, metal or timber had to be used and for obvious reasons these have not survived except where a route needed to be preserved.

This was the case at an erstwhile tramway bridge at Faenol quarry, where in fact the timbers have been renewed. This quarry was owned by Lord Newborough, less well known than say the Penrhyns, but nevertheless a significant land and quarry owner. This quarry then called Fachwen was operated by Shelton and Greaves. It was their surrendering of their lease in the 1830s on moving to Blaenau Ffestiniog, which enabled Assheton-Smith of Dinorwig to buy it and so establish a route for the Padarn Railway.

Bridge at Faenol slate quarry, on Llyn Padarn (SH578615)

The use of arches for bridging is virtually unknown where slate is involved, presumably because of the difficulty of producing suitably tapered blocks and possibly the instability inherent in slate embankments.

In granite quarries the arch was common, presumably because of the lack of long pieces and the low transverse rupture strength of the material, and in setts quarries at least, the capability of accurately trimming the arching stones.

Other timber bridges have survived by being out of reach of the casual scrounger.
Glynrhonwy Uchaf, another onetime Shelton and Greaves slate quarry was securely fenced off as an RAF bomb store.

Thus a little bridge, which once carried the tracks to a tunnel under the road, is still in situ.

Where inclines crossed over quarry terraces, it was invariably on slate slab or masonry bridges. A bridge at Cwm Machno, in wood and in situ is therefore a double

Bridge carrying an incline at Llanfairfechan Granite quarry, west of Conwy (SH693753)

rarity.

When inclines crossed terraces on the level removable bridges were used, their very portability ensured non-survival. Where tunnels intercepted underground inclines opening bridges were needed, but where a tunnel intercepted a worked out chamber quite spectacular bridges, underbraced and hung by chains from the roof were used. Such bridges would commonly have a hundred feet or more of chasm below them. The atmosphere underground was not conducive to longevity of either timber or iron and the darkness and siting made inspection difficult even with an overseer's carbide lamp. Had the void below been visible to the candle-carrying quarrymen, the use of such bridges might have

Bridge at Glynrhonwy Uchaf quarry, Llanberis (SH565607)

Incline bridge Cwm Machno quarry, near Betws-y-coed (SH751470)

Bridge over a worked-out chamber, Moel Fferna slate quarry Corwen (SJ325199)

been seriously unpopular.

Virtually every quarry and mine had rails. Ranging from a few yards of makeshift track in a tiny one or two man operation, to many miles in the big undertakings. However rails, chairs and so on make premium value and readily portable scrap, so that when a firm failed, this would be amongst the first things, seized by a landlord, sold for the benefit of creditors or just stolen!

The greatest mileage of rail remaining in situ is underground. Scrap merchants tend to shun the darkness and often one finds bare sleepers in an adit as far as some loom of daylight persists, but further in where the darkness becomes stygian, there are invariably rails slowly oxidising into oblivion.

Not all track work was melted down; some was re-laid and reused, not necessarily for similar duties. During WW1 when rails were required for trench railways in France, whole systems including standard gauge branches were

Rail at Braich Goch quarry, Corris. Probably second-hand, it could have come from the original Gorseddau Line (SH748078)

requisitioned. Much of the North Pembrokeshire and Fishguard (Nee Maenclochog) Railway, originally built to serve the Rosebush slate quarry, was lifted and shipped out (unfortunately on a vessel which was torpedoed in the English Channel).

Most re-uses were more mundane, rail can be used for fencing, bridging or to support farm building roofs. Chairs make excellent weights or doorstops.

In instances where there has never been any formal abandonment, such as was the case with the Croesor Tramway; there is an almost inexhaustible supply!

In any extractive operation using trucks on rails, track needs to be re-sited as the work-face progresses. Before modern pressed steel patent tracking became available there were several

Track underground at Cwmmaengwynedd slate quarry (SJ075236)

Chairs from Croesor Tramway make ideal gate closers (SH636459)

attempts to produce a readily portable track. One of the more successful ones was the Thomas Hughes system. The rail consisted of what was essentially round iron bar turned down at each end. The sleepers were a dog-bone iron casting with a pair of holes at either end. These holes accepted the turned down ends of the bar rail to enable lengths of track to be assembled. Additional sleepers were available to provide intermediate support for the rails.

Thomas Hughes rail at Cwm Eigiau slate quarry, to west of Dolgarrog (SH702635)

Other than the problems of curves and the truck-jarring gap where the rail-ends abutted, it was an adequate system for short internal lines and was quite popular in the early-middle years of the 19th century. Unfortunately for Mr. Hughes his rails being made from standard round bar, any competent blacksmith could readily replicate them. Casting the 'sleepers' in iron would have been more of a challenge but suitably drilled slate slabs provided a serviceable substitute.

A Slate slab drilled to act as a 'sleeper' for Thomas Hughes rail, Gorseddau Slate quarry, Cwm Pennant (SH572606). The multiple holing suggests turnout.

One frequently finds in old slate quarries small stockpiles of slates, usually in small 'damp course' sizes. Since when a quarry closed everything was normally auctioned, these are likely to be the work of 'tip boys', who particularly in hard times, would make slates by scouring the tips for block or even by dismantling walls and buildings.

The slates at Darren quarry high in the hills to the north of Machynlleth are far from being the leftovers of a beer-money hobby. Besides many part-finished gravestones and billiards table beds, there are thousands of slates or the remains of slates in the stockyard and tens of thousands on the surrounding hillside. A combination of poor quality, isolation and a depressed state of trade made them unsaleable.

Thus the fruits of possibly several man-years of work have lain unwanted in this bleak and barren wasteland for 130 years or more.

A few of the tens of thousands of slates on the ground at Darren quarry, north of Machynlleth (SH721058)

INCLINES AND HAULAGES

It has been asserted that since mines and quarries are so often situated at the tops of mountains and their markets at the bottom, the Welsh extractive industries' greatest benefactor must have been Sir Isaac Newton! There is some truth in this since much material movement was downwards. Although balanced, self-acting inclines whereby down going loaded trucks hauled up empty ones, were not invented in Wales, they were extensively used in the winning of slate, stone and metals. Towards the end of the 19th century apart from those on tramways and railways, there were upwards of a thousand self-acting inclines in operation in Welsh mines and quarries.

Several cascaded down the mountainside in multiple pitches. Others dropped almost a thousand feet in one fell swoop.

Invariably they had two tracks, up going and down going by turns, most had drum houses at the head of each pitch where a brake-controlled, horizontal drum had the endless rope wrapped around it.

The drum barrels were usually of wood, mounted on cast iron spiders, which were sold in sets complete with axle and a drum for the band brake. When in 1827 Samuel Holland opened his Gesail quarry such items were not to be had, so the whole drum had to be made of wood, presumably by the quarry's own carpenter.

In 1976 the one self-acting incline remaining in use in Wales (Rhiwbach No2) sent down its very last journey of slate trams, thus ending almost two centuries of history. It was

Wrysgan slate quarry incline, the upper part in tunnel. Plus on the Ffestiniog Railway, a Blaenau-bound train (SH678456)

Holland's upper drum house, one of the first in Blaenau Ffestiniog slate quarry, survived to the 1990s (SH688454)

Holland's drum house

Rhiw-bach no2 incline, Blaenau Ffestiniog August 1976 a week after the last load of Maenofferen slate went down. (SH707465)

Rhiw-bach no2 Incline

Drum components and winch Hen Gloddfa slate quarry, Aberllefenni near Corris (SH 761102)

retained as a showpiece, but sadly it is now derelict.

Not all planned inclines were built. At Hen Gloddfa, Aberllefenni, in the late 19th century, it was found that there was no way of dispatching slates being made at a new face at the top of the quarry. Accordingly it was planned to extend an incline and to build and equip a new drum house. A set of 3 spiders, brake drum and axle were hauled by crab winch the 500' feet or so from the valley floor.

The extension was never made and the cast iron components and the crab winch remain on site, (as do the slates!)

Part built, and most improbably located is the putative Deufaen incline. In the early 1870s, in order to take advantage of the high price of slate an attempt was made to dig on the near vertical south face of the Cnicht mountain, where even a Snowdon goat would hesitate to venture. It was planned, as at the nearby little underground Clogwyn-y-Darren working, to lower the product by ropeway from a platform cut into the hillside, to a packhorse track some hundreds of feet below. However unlike the Clogwyn's adjacent platform, the Deufaen's platform was located almost a hundred feet below the proposed adit. A steep formation down to the platform was built, but opinions differ as to whether this formation was to be an incline or a slide way. It would have been steep for an incline, unless it was of the table type, and lack of base pits suggests otherwise, the other possibility is that it was to be used as a slide until production justified the expense of tracks and drum. In the event the whole project was abandoned with no slate won when prices collapsed in 1877.

Slide way or incline? Deufaen (failed) slate digging high on the Cnicht, Cwm Croesor, Porthmadog (SH644464)

Many inclines have been totally obliterated by new work. The fine incline at Cwmorthin, which brought blocks down from the higher adits of its notoriously dangerous underground workings to its three mills, was rendered redundant in the early 1900s when the quarry was incorporated into Oakeley. It stood idle for most of a century until extensive 1990s untopping swallowed it up. Shorter, but rendered spectacular by the way it dived down through a canyon of slate waste was the incline that connected Abercwmeiddaw quarry with the Upper Corris Tramway. Idle since the 1930s, by the 1980s the great retaining walls fronting the working were yielding to the pressure of tens of thousands of tons of waste. Thus for safety reasons the walls had to be demolished and the waste profile reduced to a

Main incline at Cwmorthin slate quarry, Blaenau Ffestiniog (SH681462)

Exit incline Abercwmeiddaw slate quarry, Corris (SH746093)

prudent angle of repose.

The earlier landscaping at the nearby Braich Goch site had been more controversial. Had at least some of the surface relics been retained and conserved, a valuable visitor resource would have been created.

Nearby, at Gaewern and forming part of the same site, just a few structures remain, but what was just a few years ago an almost complete drum house, is rapidly deteriorating.

It can be argued that there are 'plenty of drum houses' indeed the skylines of Gwynedd abound with the roofless and drumless twin walls of these structures. However the number in any state of near-completeness is diminishing at an alarming rate and in spite of its state which gets sorrier by the year, this Gaewern drum house is still the best example of a self-acting drum house anywhere in Wales south of Blaenau Ffestiniog.

The Gaewern drum house is totally standard in that the two lines of track run through it under the drum. Had space at the head of incline been

Incline which connected Gaewern quarry with Braich Goch, Corris following amalgamation in 1882 (SH746084)

confined, the drum house would have been set back with the tracks curving to the left or right. In fact the variation in drums and their brake gear merits a dedicated study.

Although the horizontal drum in a drum house is the commonest form of incline headgear, sheaves on vertical axles were sometimes used. Since this is colliery haulage practice it was more common near coalfields. Such sheaves were sometimes in a structure set back from the incline head or were in a pit beneath the tracks. (It was not unknown for a drum to be set in an under-rail pit where made-up ground would not support a drum house.)

Sheaves had the advantage that when an incline had served its purpose, it was easy to re-site them elsewhere. This, rather than a lack of diligence by scrap men, is why one so often finds on a site that some, but not

Deteriorating almost by the week, drum house at Gaewern slate quarry Corris 1995 (SH745086)

Horizontal sheave at Penrhyn quarry (SH615619)

all, of the head of incline sheave pits have their sheaves missing.

The sheave arrangement on the incline, which dropped the Deeside tramway down to Glyndyfrdwy, was unique in that the sheaves were mounted neither in a housing nor a pit but above the tracks in a mock drum house. The reason presumably being to give a 'run through' while still conforming to the 'sheaves only' policy of the Deeside and Moelfferna quarries, which it served. The gear was removed to an open-air exhibition at Coedpoeth, Wrexham.

Hidden from the scrap dealer's eye, underground equipment tends to have a better survival rate than its surface counterparts. But deterioration of roofs and the sealing off of passages for safety reasons has rendered inaccessible many artefacts; such as the fine incline gear at Rhosydd. Underground, inclines could rarely be approached straight on, whereby trucks could run up or down on their own wheels. Therefore inclines were invariably of the table type enabling trucks to ride crosswise on or on turntables.

Drums were almost unknown underground, lack of space demanding that sheaves on horizontal axles be used for headgear. Lack of space sometimes prevented the usual two parallel track, double acting layout, therefore they were often single acting with a weighted trolley, running on narrow gauge rails laid between the broader gauge rails of the table to act as a counterbalance, as was the case at Rhosydd.

Self-acting, gravity inclines, whether underground or on the surface are fine for down going loads, but with up going loads, gravity does not oblige. The very nature of mineral

Overhead Sheaves Deeside Tramway Glyndyfrdwy, Corwen (SJ149425)

Deeside Tramway looking towards incline

extraction implies raising and raising requires power.

Power for lifting was a big challenge in mining and quarrying.

At its most basic, this could involve a hand-cranked windlass, or on a slightly more sophisticated level a horse whim, where a horse walked around in a circle to work a winder.

A water wheel or turbine sometimes wound an incline but this was not the best use of a limited resource which might be better applied to other duties.

Steam was expensive and not ideal for intermittent duties, but until oil engines became available it was often the only option. Oil was also best suited for continuous loads such as air compression or electric generation. Indeed up to the 1950s, in some remote areas oil engines were the most practicable way to generate the electricity that was the

Head sheave tensioner 3-6 incline underground at Rhosydd slate quarry, Blaenau Ffestiniog (SH664461)

Incline table 3-6 incline Rhosydd

ideal power for inclines and haulages.

Powered inclines were used in coal and other mines, but the most spectacular were in slate workings.

The fine main exit incline at Llechwedd was originally steam powered, but probably because of the heavy currents needed by large motors, continued to use steam even after their pioneering hydro-generating plant was installed. It was electrified during WW1 when the steam engine was requisitioned by the then Minister for Munitions David Lloyd George to power shell making at the Boston Lodge works of the Ffestiniog Railway. This fine multi-track incline was quarried away by opencast working in the 1980s.

Inclein Bôn at Llechwedd slate quarry Blaenau Ffestiniog (SH700470)

The last two inclines to operate in the Welsh slate industry were those underground at Maenofferen, which up-hauled product to mills level. The remarkable thing about them was the continued use of brine barrel resistors.

The principle of varying electric current by raising and lowering metal plates into a concentrated solution of brine was an early way of controlling heavy motors. The controllers for both the Maenofferen inclines were the earliest form of such controllers, being three actual barrels of brine (one per phase). Copper plates suspended on cords from co-axial pulleys could be lowered into the brine when the banksman paid out a cord onto a fourth pulley. This arrangement worthy of a Heath Robinson cartoon nevertheless operated on a daily basis for almost 90 years. The only concession to modernity being the substitution of plastic dustbins for the casks on the controller for the lower incline.

Maenofferen was, with the exception of Aberllefenni, the last user of railed wagons in the slate industry and had the last of the underground mess rooms or Cabanau, which had

Winding house Inclen Bôn Llechwedd

been such a feature of social and cultural life of northwestern Meirionnydd. Its closure meant the end of the underground working which had epitomised Blaenau Ffestiniog for almost two centuries.

Brine Bath resistors Maenofferen (SH715467) slate quarry. The plates are raised so cutting off the current. The control rope is wound around the wheel on the left

A simple and economical way of using water for up-haulage was the water balance. These had a table on one track and a tank on the other. When the tank was filled its weight could raise the table and a loaded truck, when it was emptied the weight of the table and an unladen truck could raise the tank. They could be made double acting by having a combined tank and table on each track. Such devices were inherently slow but were quite widely used, in slate, metal mining and in coal. Vestiges of tanks and other artefacts exist, as well as incline formations, usually distinguishable from other inclines by one

A slab wagon, restrained by a crimp gate waits to be lowered, lower incline Maenofferen

track not being identical with the other, as well as possible evidence of pipes or storage tanks.

The only near complete examples are two at Aberllefenni which were used to lift slate quarrying waste to the tops of tips.

The same principle was also used for vertical lifts

Water balances were rare underground. Where they operated below natural drainage level, the tank instead of running parallel to the load table would run in a sloping tunnel or shaft at a higher level, acting by means of ropes and pulleys.

They were used in underground slate workings around Blaenau Ffestiniog at, for instance Rhosydd and Croesor, but the one at Cambrian quarry may well have been an unique underground example outside the Blaenau area.

The use of haulage underground in slate

Water balanced incline at Aberllefeni (SH768102)/ Due to rope failure both table and tank are at the bottom of this short incline

Water balanced incline tank. The sheet metal has rusted away but the valve identifies its purpose. Underground Cambrian slate quarry. Glyn Ceiriog (SJ189378)

workings was by no means confined to permanent installations. Heavy block needed to be moved and lifted onto wagons, often in confined situations. Both hand and power winches were used, usually acting through ropes reeved through sheaves hung from the roofs of chambers.

Hand winches from sailing ships made useful crab winches and steam donkey engines could be run off the compressed air supply, which from around the 1890s was laid on in workings for rock drilling.

Such winches are portable, useful and make such good scrap, that it is extremely rare to find them except in the most inaccessible locations or where they have been built in as a permanent installation.

The inclines and indeed all the systems at Rhosydd are thoroughly documented in Rhosydd by Lewis & Denton.

Ship's steam winch underground Braich Goch slate quarry Corris (SH748078)

Hand winch underground at Braich Goch slate quarry

ROPEWAYS

Aerial ropeways were widely used in collieries for the dumping of waste, in metal mining for moving ore and in stone quarrying. They were almost unknown in slate workings but a variation, the chain incline, where loads were up-hauled suspended from a cable rather than up a railed ramp, was used in many open-pit extractive industries, as they could be readily re-sited whereas a fixed incline formation could not.

Chain inclines could only pick up from a single point, but the deepening of slate pits in the late 19th century led to their being terrace worked calling for multiple pick up points. This led to the development of the 'Blondin', where a carriage running on a catenary wire spanning a pit from pillars were able to pick up from any point directly beneath it. These were used in several slate quarries, but the 'home' of such installations was the Nantlle valley, south of Caernarfon. There, a number of quarries worked pits hundreds of feet deep. Several had a number in simultaneous use. The last user was Penyrorsedd, which lifted everything out of their working this way until a road down into the pit was built in the late 1970s.

Blondin Tower Penyrorsedd slate quarry, Nantlle valet (SH510538)

Dinorwig and Penrhyn slate quarries at Llanberis and Bethesda respectively were basically hillside quarries working terraces, but due to the vagaries of the veins did have some pit working, and both used Blondins.

Although Penrhyn's ropeways had not been used since the 1960s some remained in situ until succumbing to the advance of the workings in the 1990s.

Some early Blondins were steam driven but their intermittent operation made electricity, when it became available, a more

One of the last trucks to be lifted on a Blondin. Penyrorsedd 1976 (SH510538)

Blondin tower Penrhyn quarry (SH620650)

Blondin Tower Penrhyn

economical power source. The winders used for a Blondin differed from a standard winder in having two (Coaxial) drums, one for lifting and one controlling the position of the carriage.

Blondin winding house Penrhyn

Electric Blondin winch, Penrhyn

CRANES

Cranes are one of the most fundamental of machines for anything but the lightest of industries. Cranes were not much used in slate working other than in the mills. Elsewhere lifting was generally by sheer legs and winch, a hazardous operation since if the ratchet failed the handle would backspin devastatingly

Where cranes were employed, due to their portability and desirability both for reuse and for scrap it is most unusual for them to be found in abandoned workings.

An exception was the derrick at Hafodlas, which due to subsequent work became marooned, where it remained until the rotting of its wooden legs caused it to plunge to destruction in the 1980s

Wood was usual in Scotch derricks, but was also surprisingly common in workshop cranes, both of the wall jib and pillar types as well as travelling overhead gantries.

Sound, well-maintained wood can resist rot and parasitic attack almost indefinitely indoors, but most have long fallen foul of insurance inspectors.

Abandoned crane at Hafolas slate quarry Betws-y-coed (SH779562)

Wooden foundry crane Players tinplate works, Clydach, Swansea (SN688010)

To make a crane from wood using one's own carpenter had obvious advantages over buying in an iron one, but they were found in iron foundries which could have presumably produced them on site. The 'Players' crane was installed in the then Clydach Forge by Mr J.J. Strick probably in the late 1850s, remaining in use for over a century.

Claimed in the 1970s to be the oldest crane in everyday use was the crane at Pentresaeson foundry near Wrexham. It allegedly came from the Bersham

Wooden foundry Crane Pentresaeson, near Wrexham (SJ278532)

Crane at John Mills 'Railway Foundry' Llanidloes (SN958845)

ironworks; if this is so it could well have dated from the 1790s. Regrettably it was broken up c1980.

Another serious loss was the cast iron crane at the Llanidloes works of Messrs John Mills. This engineering works was originally the workshops for the Newtown and Llanidloes Railway, which became the Mid-Wales Railway, later being absorbed into the Cambrian Railways. Installed in 1858, the crane standing on its original base remained in use in 'passed inspection' state until being scrapped c1980.

Fortunately not all redundant cranes are scrapped!

A wall crane, acts as a display rack in Messrs Reid's warehouse at Cilgerran, Aberteifi. The building was the sawing mill for the Plain slate quarry and the crane would have been used for lifting blocks onto the saw-tables.

Plain had one of the last, or if not the last, the most bizarre, horse-worked incline in Wales. There was no whim or winder, a pulley at the incline head enabled a trolley to be pulled up a slope by a horse walking along the adjacent public road!

Wall crane in Reid's warehouse Cilgerran which was Plain quarry mill (SN203428)

MACHINES

Almost all industries use machinery, machinery which when redundant or when operations cease, is usually sold off, for reuse or for scrap. Even where there was no sale, it may well have mysteriously disappeared! Thus in abandoned workings, plant is usually only to be found at inaccessible locations.

Although the numbers gradually diminish, in slate workings at least, machines in varying states of decay and incompleteness are still to be found.

The commonest are slate dressing machines, almost always of the Greaves type, which have a rotating 'lawn mower' blade. Normally power driven, some of the first were hand cranked. The operator wound it up to speed then tried to trim as many slates as he could before it slowed down too much to use.

Although these unpowered versions have been obsolete for

Very early (1850s?) hand-cranked Greaves dressing machine Llechwedd (SH700470)

Early dressing machine in re-use at Croes y Ddwy Afon slate quarry 1980s (SH754424)

a century or more, due to its extra size one such machine remained in use at Llechwedd quarry Blaenau Ffestiniog until the late 1990s.

A slightly later variation, operated by a pedal, remained, at the nearby Maenofferen quarry right up to its closure

Early machines turned out by local foundries, were usually mounted on wooden bases made by the quarry carpenter.

Later they were produced in large numbers, with integral iron bases by Messrs Turner of Newtown. One example was for years at Llandeilo, a small slate quarry in Pembrokeshire. It is unusual in that it was designed to be driven either by pulley or by treadle. The fact that it has a safety guard reveals its late (1950s) use. There were at least eight of these same machines in Pembrokeshire (One is now in the Museum of Welsh Slate, Llanberis) and it is probable that

Pedal-driven dresser Maenofferen (SH715467)

Greaves pattern dresser made by Turner of Newtown. Llandeilo quarry Pembrokeshire (SN104272)

they were all part of a batch ordered in 1875 for Rosebush quarry. Their use there high on the terraces rather than in the mill accounts for the treadle option, but there has been speculation that the pulleys were for an intended wind power source.

The Greaves type rotary dresser was not considered suitable for the hard Cambrian slate of northern Caernarfonshire or parts of the Mawddach area.

There, slates were either dressed by hand or by using Amos & Francis dressers. These guillotines had a hinged blade operated by a pedal and were a speciality of De Winton of Caernarfon.

Whilst improved versions of Greaves dressers remain in use, the guillotine machine at Bethesda was the last complete on-site survivor and may well have been the last to have been used.

The other basic machine for slate

Francis pattern dresser Coed y Parc, Bethesda (SH615663)

Fragment of a sand saw Melynllyn hone quarry, Dolgarrog (SH705654)

reduction was the saw. The earliest form of saw for cutting any stone was the sand saw, which had a toothless iron blade, reciprocated by water power, it cut by introducing wet sand into the saw kerf. One of the few remnants is, or was, just a wheel and crank in the ruins of a building at Melynllyn high above Cwm Eigiau in the shadow of Carnedd Llywelyn, in one of the remotest spots in Wales. This was a quarry producing hones, or sharpening stones, which closed in 1908.

Carreg Jasper quarry

Frame of Gang Saw Carreg quarry Aberdaron (SH162292)

The successor to the sand saw was the gang saw in which a frame carrying several saw blades was swung to and fro suspended from a massive steel frame. These were never thick on the ground but the frame of one survives at Carreg quarry near Aberdaron. Opened in 1904, to make jasper rock gravestones, much prized by the wealthy of Merseyside, and by those nearer at hand whose status seemed to their progeny to merit memorialisation in a material other than the slate which marked the sleep of lesser mortals.

More typical of slate working were circular saws, which remained in use until high-speed diamond saws replaced the last of them in about 1970. Since these are hefty pieces of kit they have

Remains of a saw table Lefel Dur Oer, Graig Ddu (SH718455)

considerable scrap value, so few survived long after they became idle and few if any survive today outside of exhibitions.

The standard saw took several forms, but were all variations of the original Greaves mid 19th century patents.

A blade of 20' or so diameter protruded up through a moveable table. These tables invariably had a pattern of square holes to accommodate wedges to secure the block being sawn.

Except for the earliest saws which had chain-pulled tables, saw tables were advanced by a rack and pinion driven from the saw spindle by a double worm gear train incorporating an automatic return.

Such circular saws suffered from the shortcoming that the speed at which the table was advanced was determined by the speed of the saw blade. The ratio could be specified so that tables of saws intended for

Fragments of the table of a hand-cranked saw Darren Quarry, Machynlleth (SH721058)

Remains of an hydraulic-feed saw Penyrorsedd, Nantlle (SH510538)

use with hard rock could be made to advance at a slower rate than those meant for soft rock. Some quarries had several saws with different feed rates and there was at least one attempt to incorporate a three-speed gear. None could cope with varying hardness in an individual block or allow for the gradual blunting of the saw blade and one can find sawn-ends where the cut wavers due to the forcing of a blunt saw blade.

Where no power was available small hand-cranked circular saws were used which differed from power saws in that the table was advanced by a weight and pulleys. This was an almost ideal situation since with a block being pressed against the saw by a constant pressure; the feed rate was self-correcting. The size of weight required would have precluded this system for power saws. Until electronic control became available in the late 20th century, there had been only one attempt at making a constant-pressure feed power saw. This used a hydraulic cylinder and was incorporated into a batch of saws supplied to Penyrorsedd slate quarry at Nantlle by the De Winton Company in the 1870s. Unfortunately at that time suitable pumps, actuators, hoses and fluids were not to be had. Thus in spite of the theoretical advantages of the system, and interest shown by other quarries no further examples were made.

The few that survived Penyrorsedd's various 20th century vicissitudes were scrapped in the 1990s, but happily one is preserved at the Welsh Slate Museum.

The other machines used in slate workings were planers, used for smoothing slab products. When, around the 1850s, planers began to be used, planed flooring flags and so on could command a substantial premium over 'as split' items, the latter eventually becoming almost unsaleable.

As a consequence there was an immediate demand for planing machines which local foundries hastened to devise and manufacture.

When the ubiquitous Turner Brothers entered this market their substantial machines with automatic feed, based on engineering planers, supplanted the relatively flimsy, hand-fed offerings of the local makers.

One at Gloddfa Ganol, Blaenau Ffestiniog, was in the process of being restored as an exhibit when a change of ownership resulted in it being scrapped in 1997.

Early slate planer, Gloddfa Ganol, Blaenau Ffestiniog (SH694470)

PUMPING

Vital to most mining and quarrying operations were pumps. These could vary from portable hand pumps to big steam and later, electric systems.

The earliest type of pump was the Rag and Chain where greasy rags on an endless chain were dragged up a vertical pipe lifting water in the process. From the earliest times until the price of iron fell following the Napoleonic wars, these were often made by hollowing-out tree trunks.

Remains of a hollowed-out tree trunk, part of a Rag & Chain pump Drws y Coed copper mine (SH545534)

Such early pumps would where possible have been water powered. Water wheels did suffer from drought and freezing problems, but apart from their 'fuel' being free, their ability to carry on unattended day and night, meant that they remained in use long after engines and motors were available. This was particularly true in 'part time' workings where men possibly employed in mining or quarrying would dig as a paying hobby. Such a working was Nant Gefail y Meinars a tiny, remote mine which sought gold but which may have raised a little copper.

Most pumping was on a more major scale and if a water wheel was used it might have to be sited up to half a mile or more from the pump, operating through reciprocating flat-rods, which were either supported on rollers or on hinged pillars. For many years a vast bell crank of the pump at Allt Ddu slate quarry, which was associated with Dinorwig, remained in place until the 1980s landscaping.

Pumping wheel at Nant Gefail y Meinars mine near Ffestiniog (SH768395)

Pumps were not

always large, fixed installations; small accumulations of water were moved with hand pumps. The hand pump found underground at Moelfferna slate quarry, was still in good working order over 30 years after it had been abandoned

Pump bob Allt Ddu quarry before landscaping (SH591610)

At tiny, shallow workings such as Nant Gefail y Meinars, raising a few bucketfuls of ore by hand presented no challenge; the water wheel could be devoted to pumping

For deeper and more substantial undertakings, a water wheel might combine winding with the pumping. It would have been usual for the wheel to be permanently connected to the pump, with a clutch allowing the winding drum to be engaged when required.

A very well known example of this is at Cwm Ciprwth, a copper mine in Cwm Pennant north of Porthmadog. The wheel and mechanism was almost certainly second-hand and only operated for a few years in the 1890s. Fortunately its remote location protected it from both scrap men and vandals. Seriously degraded, it was restored by the Snowdonia National Park in the 1990s.

Unusual siting has ensured the survival in near working order of a remarkable 16' waterwheel at Ystrad Einon lead mine near Aberystwyth. Installed underground in the 1880s, it pumped and wound a 24-fathom winze. There have been proposals to remove it for exhibition, but it is to be hoped that efforts to do this will not succeed, since this

Hand pump underground at Moelfferna slate working near Corwen (SJ125399)

Pumping/winding wheel Cwm Ciprwth before restoration (SH526478)

Underground water wheel Ystrad Einon, Aberystwyth (SN707938)

would totally destroy its provenance. However perhaps at some time in the future some arrangements for public viewing can be made.

VENTILATION

All underground workings require ventilation, particularly coal mines, which can generate both explosive and asphyxiating gases.

Waddle fan at a Mountain Ash colliery, south Wales

The earliest form of assisted ventilation was a fire lit at the bottom of the up-cast shaft. Although this primitive procedure came to be supplanted by fans, it was in fact more efficient in terms of air moved per ton of coal burnt, than any mechanical device.

One colliery extractor fan in almost worldwide use was the Waddle fan. Devised and produced by a Llanelli firm which having been founded in 1815 was arguably the oldest firm in the town when it closed in the 1980s.

Fan house Croesor slate quarry (SH657457)

Few non-coal mines required forced ventilation, most being able to rely on natural circulation, downward in summer and upward in winter, reflecting the almost constant temperature underground. Most underground slate workings, except those with only one adit or having steam engines inside the workings, managed with just a brattice screen or two to direct the natural flow.

One such exception was Croesor which was ventilated with a most elegantly housed fan, which forced air into the main tunnel. Long after the rest of the site had been razed this fine structure remained almost intact until it was dismantled to be exhibited at Gloddfa Ganol at Blaenau Ffestiniog. Regrettably this never happened.

Slate workings may not have needed ventilation underground, but it was a different matter in the mills where slate was sawn, trimmed and planed. Vainly relying on open doorways to carry away the dust, slate sawing and trimming was traditionally conducted in an impenetrable and deadly fog.

Discarded extractor fan Penyrorsedd, Nantlle (SH510538)

Modern legislation enforces the installation of extractors, which, since it took almost as much power to de-dust a traditional-type saw as to drive it, was a drain on tight budgets and the requirement may well have hastened some mid-20th century closures.

Happily the modern diamond saws, lanishers and so on, working under a copious water drench, do not create such a problem.

Ironically now that the health risks posed by mechanical working seem to have been overcome, it has been found that the non-mechanical splitting process also generates dust in particulate but nevertheless dangerous form.

POWER

Water wheel, Felindre near Swansea (SN638027)

All machinery needs power, and fortunately the topography and rainfall of Wales provided abundant, fast flowing water and from the earliest times the water wheel was the standard power source for flour, and woollen mills. The prevalence of the place name Felindre (mill place) emphasises the importance of mills. As industry developed many of these sites were hijacked for works and factories.

During the 19th century the number of water wheels for every purpose multiplied, but of the thousands there once were, only a score or two remain.

A few are working for demonstration, or are in some cases still grinding corn. The majority just rot, but hopefully some, such as the wheel of the Felindre Mill near Swansea will be restored.

More efficient than the water wheel is the Pelton wheel. Pelton wheel rotors are commonly seen and many complete machines remain in use, their number increasing as small hydro-electric stations come on line, Pelton wheels are impulse devices which depend on water pressure, but turbines depend on flow so that where water head is limited turbines are used.

Turbine from Plas Tan y Bwlch, Maentwrog awaits restoration

Water turbine, Oakeley quarry, Blaenau Ffestiniog (SH695470)

(Large modern hydro-electric stations use turbines due to the size limitation on Peltons), sadly few survive. The turbine, which powered one of the first electric plants in Wales at Plas Tan y Bwlch, has been rescued and is under restoration, but the big turbine at Oakeley slate quarry went for scrap a few weeks after this picture was taken.

Oddly there have been places in Wales where there was insufficient water! Industries near hilltops lacked catchment and those in lowlands lacked speed of flow. Even in famously wet Blaenau Ffestiniog, the concentration of power demand meant that steam, expensive though it was, had to be widely used.

Whilst steam avoided the stoppages of drought or frost it was far from ideal for some uses. It was suitable where power demand was reasonably continuous, such as in textile mills, rolling mills and furnace blowers. Steam pressure had to be wastefully maintained for intermittent and variable duties such as winding, workshops and slate mills. Pumping was continuous, but

Turbine rotor

called for night manning and with coal in remote areas costing treble its pithead price, costly.

Just as water wheels could be multi use, so steam engines frequently pumped and wound, at Rhiw-bach slate quarry (SH740462) one engine drove a mill and wound three inclines, and possibly wound a shaft. Such stationary engines were invariably sold complete or totally scrapped so relics are few.

Similarly scarce are remains of portable engines, which were based around a standard locomotive or traction engine firebox and smoke tube boiler, usually with an engine on top of it. Mounted on wheels they could be readily moved by a horse to be re-sited as need arose.

Paradoxically one of the most complete examples of this type of engine, at Cwt y Bugail slate quarry, is not strictly a portable engine at all, but is in fact an old traction engine of the type much used to haul industrial loads in pre-motor lorry times. It has two winding drums one of which directly raised rubbish to pass across an adjacent weighbridge; the other drum powered an underground incline via a lengthy rope zigzagging around pulleys.

There was, incidentally, another multi-use on this same site since the mill engine also hauled wagons. Furthermore at the adjacent Blaen y Cwm quarry, the steam engine which powered the incline also backed-up the mill water wheel.

Traction engine at Cwt y Bugail slate quarry (SH734469)

Whilst engines are saleable, boilers are not. Engines can be reduced to manageable pieces with sledgehammers, boilers call for gas-cutting equipment, use of which their scrap value tends not to justify. Thus abandoned boilers are more common than the engines they fed, although the presence of a boiler is no evidence of the use of steam, since a failed-inspection boiler can provide a cheap container for water or fuel oil. (For whatever purpose, how some boilers reached the remote heights where they now lie can be puzzling).

A curious though sadly incomplete engine is that which drove the Wrysgan

Brake ratchet identifies it as road vehicle

Pulley mount

Lancashire boiler Fron-boeth quarry (SH652448)

slate quarry 'gravity' incline. This incline is itself unusual, since the upper part is in a tunnel, was badly graded so would not self-act. A steam engine was installed, but due to an inadequate boiler, it never worked satisfactorily.

The coming on stream of the Maentwrog hydro station enabled the mill to be electrically driven, but a second motor for the incline could not be afforded so the mill motor was unbolted and temporally installed at the incline head whenever a load had to be sent down the incline!

Ultimately a lorry engine was used.

Fragments of incline engine, Wrysgan (SH678456)

From around the 1900s, gas-oil, petrol, Diesel or those very dodgy devices, producer gas engines, began to take over from steam particularly for air compression and electric generation. Like stationary steam units, they tended to be scrapped or re-used, so other than those deliberately preserved, very few survive.

More commonly found, gradually degrading into rust and dust on hillsides, are the various adaptations of vehicle engines used to power small scale quarrying operations.

At Wrysgan, besides the lorry engine used to drive the exit incline, a car gearbox, evidence of the use of another engine

The later lorry engine

Gearbox of car engine, Wrysgan

Car engine Cwt y Bugail (SH734469)

Winch Cwt y Bugail

Remains of a tractor, Cwt y Bugail

(allegedly from the manager's Lea Francis!), which was used to wind an internal, incline.

The 1960s re-working of Cwt y Bugail slate quarry involved some tricky haulage and lifting challenges. Competitiveness demanded mechanical means, but lack of both funds and throughput precluded any great expenditure.

Curiously, following the most unusual earlier use of a steam traction engine as a power source on this site, an old agricultural tractor was somehow lowered into the pit to drive a temporary haulage.

METAL MINES

Mention of metal mining in Wales suggests gold mining by the Romans at Pumsaint in Carmarthenshire. In fact most Welsh gold was found along the north bank of the Mawddach mainly from around 1840 to the early 20th century, with some activity in the 1920s and 30s, and again in the 1980s and 90s.

Glamorous gold mining may have been, but profitable it was not. Of some 60 mines, only a third recorded anything more than derisory outputs, nearly all coming from just two, Clogau and Gwynfynydd.

Apart from a few very brief bonanzas, gold-bearing rock averaged a yield of under a half ounce per ton, which could only be released after lengthy and costly crushing, stamping, washing, separating and so on, often by methods little changed in millennia. Some mines had machinery, but it was by no means unknown for rock to be crushed by pounding it with stones on a stone anvil. In fact in some of the tiny marginal workings a hammer and iron anvil would have been regarded as 'Hi-tech'

The output of Welsh gold in world terms was

Gwynfynydd, drum of a balanced incline is believed to be the only one at a Welsh gold mine. Lack of weather protection, must have caused brake problems (SH737283)

'Deep Adit, Gwynfynydd gold mine, during 1980s revival

trifling. The total production of the Dolgellau gold belt, would fit into a 2' cube. Worth millions in modern money but scarcely matching the overall capital expenditure, let alone the toil of hundreds of men over several generations.

Welsh gold mining was not so much a matter of riches springing from the ground as riches being poured into it. However, such is the lure of gold that there was never a lack of entrepreneurs ready to wager on outside chances nor gullible investors prepared to back them. Doubtless we shall see more of both in the future.

Far larger and much more profitable than gold was lead mining. This grew rapidly with the ending of the Crown monopoly in the 17th century and the amount of silver found in the Ceredigion lead mines was enough to justify a Royal Mint at Aberystwyth.

Lead was mainly used in the grander houses for roof flashings, snow-boxes, kitchen sinks and so on, but with the growth of piped water during the 19th century, demand expanded and substantial mines developed at Minera and

Gwynfynydd, kibble being drawn up a winze, 1980s

Prince Edward gold mine, Trawsfynydd, 'Wishing Well' windlass underground (SH743385)

elsewhere in the Wrexham-Mold area. The Van mine near Llanidloes was particularly successful, and there were numerous workings in the Conwy valley and in Carmarthenshire.

Towards the end of the 19th century competition from overseas sources, producing richer ores on a bigger scale, robbed Welsh lead of its markets. Fortunately zinc was often found in congruous veins so with the rise of galvanising a number of lead mines were able to re-invent themselves as zinc mines.

Other metals included manganese, demand for which expanded with the late 19th century need for specialist steels. The mines north of Barmouth and on the Llŷn peninsular proved of strategic importance during two world wars.

Iron was widely mined, literally from the Iron Age, up to the 1960s, when the last mine, at Llanharry in Glamorgan, closed.

However, although total output was less than that of lead, the king of Welsh metal was copper, the mining and smelting of which dominated world trade.

NOT a colliery but Halkyn West lead mine (SJ201698)

More typical of a lead mine Nant y Garw Elan Valley (SN899651)

Work initiated by Mr. Duncan James in the 1960s/70s has shown that copper was being mined at Llandudno during the second millennium BC. From this developed a trade with Cornwall for tin for bronze manufacture, leading to an association lasting almost to the present day. That county not only supplied Wales with mine captains, but also much of the water-powered winding and pumping gear as well as the eponymous steam engines. In fact the decline of Cornish mining co-incided with the rise of Welsh coal mining, with the result that many second-hand engines were available, to the detriment of Welsh manufacturers such as the Neath Abbey Iron Company and De Winton of Caernarfon.

In the late 18th century the Parys copper mine on Anglesey was the largest in the world, but by the early 19th century its importance had declined. By then copper mining was mainly centred in Snowdonia, with several mines so remotely sited that output had to be carried in sacks on men's

Mineralisation underground at Parys copper mine, Amlwch (SH444905)

The Royal Cambrian Company's unsuccessful copper trials at Moelwyn near Blaenau Ffestiniog. (SH656448)

backs.

In the early 19th century big international financiers became interested in Welsh copper, forming the Royal Cambrian company. This company was unsuccessful but its successor, the Welsh Slate Company succeeded spectacularly, eventually having the largest slate operation in Blaenau Ffestiniog.

Copper mining also flourished a little to the south on the Mawddach and it was discoveries of gold in mines such as St Davids and Glasdir which kick-started the gold activity in that area.

There was a downside to this Welsh pre-eminence. The near monopoly of the Swansea smelters enabled them to control ore prices and their efforts to keep prices low may well have hastened the decline of indigenous mining.

Not all mining was for metal, coal or slate. Building stone was mined near Bala; the high-grade limestone being used for building Bala College.

An Arastra at St Davids copper/gold working. A unique example of a primitive Central American device whereby a tapered stone is pushed around a circle to crush ore (SH667197)

Graig y Fron Limestone mine (SH973371)

WALKING TO WORK

Walking? How else would you get there? Factory workers, dockers and most colliers, lived close to their work, (although some pitmen did have a long walk underground). Shop assistants and domestic servants often lived on the premises, their hours might be long but their journey to work took only seconds! Not so industrial workers in rural areas such as metal meinars and quarrymen.

Agricultural workers often had a distance to travel before spending the day on their feet, but few had the monumental journeys faced by many men in quarries and metal mines. A daily five mile each way walk was not exceptional, even after train travel became possible, it was often shunned in order to save the few pence fare.

Zigzag steps Oakeley quarry Blaenau Ffestiniog (SH690466)

Quarrymen, even if they lived close by, might still be faced with a daunting climb of hundreds of feet before starting their day's work. After perhaps ten punishing hours, there would be an equally long descent, which in summer might be followed by an evening tending a smallholding. In pit workings the order would be reversed, so that there might well be a daunting climb up a series of ladders.

That was just the main workforce. By the time they had reached their workplaces on a cold and wet morning, the enginemen would have been at work for two hours or more raising steam.

In some cases enginemen had cottages adjacent to their engine, but most would have the same journey as their workmates, except that in the winter darkness, it was they who had to beat a track through the drifted snow.

Workers who could reach home in the evenings, would for a few hours enjoy a modicum of comfort with their families. Those who lived further afield could not. In both slate working and metal mining many men would spend the week in barracks, leaving home in the small hours of Monday morning, returning late on Saturday afternoon. The distances were daunting. The writer knew a Mr Griffiths whose father would walk from Beddgelert to Pen-y-pass and on up the Meinars Track to Britannia copper mine a distance of more than twelve miles and a climb of almost 2000'. At least he had road or cart track the whole way. The father of the late Mr Chris Hughes of Dolwyddelan worked at Rhiw-bach, much of his six miles or so involved stiff climbs on sheep tracks. Acceptable on a nice dry moonlight night but not when plunging through morasses in driving rain in pitch darkness. Some of the men at Cwm Eigiau quarry were from Bethesda; they had anything up to ten miles of almost entirely trackless walk, which took them up to 3000' at Foel-grach.

Access ladders at Penyrorsedd, Nantlle (SH510538)

These journeys make nice recreational walks on a summer's day, but certainly not nice and far from recreational in pitch darkness, in a blizzard, in leaky boots, protected not by Gore-Tex but by an old sack.

Tolerable perhaps if one was looking forward to a hot bath, dry clothes and central heating. There would be no bath and no dry clothes, since they would be going straight to work possibly still in torrential rain and biting wind.

When at the end of the day, the barracks was finally reached, the only way the heating would be central was if the stove was in the middle! A fire could only be lit if

Barracks, Rhosydd (SH664461)

Access steps made from slate sleepers Vivian quarry Llanberis (SH586605)

Slate stile near Bethesda

wood or peat had been gathered and dried. Only then could a meal be cooked from the week's rations that each man had brought, and attempts made to dry sodden clothing. The only bath would be a dip in the works pond.

These journeys were not always by men going to work; some less remote sites had family accommodation so that wives needed to shop and children to attend school. There is an instance of a pre-teen girl living at the Moelwyn slate working who attended school at Tanygrisau, more than 1000' lower down the bare mountain.

Some of these routes are still well used tracks, such as the 'Meinars Track' to Snowdon, others are just traces of what now seem like paths which lead from nowhere to nowhere.

Movement within working areas was not always easy even to a rockman used to hanging from a rope wrapped around his thigh, or a miner accustomed to perching on a footboard in a stope..

In slate workings there was widespread use of cantilever steps, which are, (one is assured!) much stronger than they appear.

The finest example of such steps was at Abercwmeiddaw, Upper Corris, which visitors were more ready to admire than to use! Sadly they had to be landscaped due to the instability of the revetment.

There used to be many other examples of cantilevered steps but these are becoming fewer as time and as necessary (and unnecessary) safety demolitions are carried out. A few still remain and indeed some

Cantilever steps, Abercwmeiddaw, Corris (SH746093)

Cantilevered steps give access to brakeman's place atop an electric winding house Diffwys quarry, Blaenau Ffestiniog (SH712463)

are available for public use, such as those that gave access to Aberllefenni station on the Corris railway.

Steps did not have to be cantilevered to make their use appear unwise.

At Llaneilian slate quarry solitarily perched on an Anglesey cliff top, the integrity of the steps was obviously sound, hewn as they were out of the solid rock, but the siting! Cut into the cliff face, windswept and even wave swept they provided access to a platform inside an enlarged cave. This cave provided a covered dock where a boat could be loaded with slate lowered down a shaft from the quarry high above.

A number of cliff-top slate workings in the Tintagel area lowered material into ships moored below and there were direct-into-boat arrangements on the Pembrokeshire coast, but this Llaneilian facility, reminiscent of WW2 U-boat pens is apparently quite unique.

Underground too, movement was hazardous. Underfoot slate could be just as wet and slippery as on the surface, added to which, in the almost stygian darkness drops and precipices could be unseen, defects in bridges, stagings and so on might pass unnoticed. In fact falling from height was the commonest causes of fatal and serious injury accidents

Cliff face steps, Llaneilian slate quarry Anglesey (SH481925)

In underground slate working not much use was made of ladders, ascents and descents could usually be made on steps alongside inclines or on the slopes of backfilled waste. In some instances there were man-riding facilities on inclines.

If ladders were used they were usually short and invariably of iron.

Not so in metal mining where shafts possibly hundreds of feet deep had to be negotiated by ladders, usually of wood in conditions perfect for the growth of every kind of rot.

Actually, unlike say Cornwall, great depths were rare in

Welsh metal mining; even so insecure ladders and rickety platforms provided plenty of opportunities for injury.

The only metal mines to have colliery-type cages were some of the deeper and more modern lead workings in the Mold area.

Iron ladder underground Craig Rhiweirth slate quarry (SJ053262)

Ladder Gwynfynedd gold mine during 1980s working, (SH737283)

HOMES & BUILDINGS

Where industries develop the workers they attract need homes.

Some houses were built speculatively, some by the employers. Together they created the terraces, which cling to the sides of industrial valleys. Just a few departed from the standard, 'sold by the yard'ranks and tiers, some such as the Square at Blaenavon being imaginatively laid out to foster a community spirit. The outstanding example of good layout and, by the standards of the time, good accommodation, was the Merthyr Triangle, built by the Plymouth ironworks and destroyed by Authority in one of the most flagrant acts of official vandalism since the time of Genghis Khan.

On a more modest scale were the houses provided by smaller employers. The Tai Glas (Blue cottages) built by Aberllefenni slate quarry, now part demolished, had for

'Merthyr Triangle' (SO056052)

'Blue cottages' Aberllefenni (SH766104)

instance, fenestration detail that went much beyond the utilitarian.

Nor was all speculative building to be deplored. By grouping four units round a single chimney cluster the Tai Incorn at Blaenau Ffestiniog enabled dwellings to be built and offered for rent at minimum cost. This, together with one door and small windows, helped to make them what we would now call 'energy efficient', an important consideration in a town of harsh climate and high coal prices. Not necessarily the sort of dwelling we would relish today but in the mid 19th century very much better than many hovels then being hastily thrown up.

Industrial workers living in towns lacked the opportunity to supplement their wages by growing vegetables and keeping a pig or a cow. Those living in small mining and quarrying communities could do this, as certainly could those in the self-built cottages which still dot the hillsides of north Caernarfonshire and elsewhere.

This widespread practice of industrial workers having a smallholding gives rise to confusion among

Tai Uncorn, Blaenau Ffestiniog

Cottage, Llanberis (SH558608)

researchers. Anyone occupying more than the most trifling plot would describe himself at census times as 'farmer', an occupation carrying a higher social status than that of miner or quarryman.

One disadvantage of country dwelling today is the lack of local shops.

In the 19th century this does not seem to have been a problem. The tiny settlement of R'alltgoed comprised R'alltgoed Hall, a quarry manager's house, a manse and a terrace of four houses, one of which was a shop! With no passing trade, the couple of farms being almost self-sufficient and the quarrymen bringing in their own food, trade must have been thin.

Sadly, apart from the Hall itself, the whole hamlet, including the chapel is now little more than rubble.

Nearby, a tiny but relatively important building, the 'Bell House' at Aberllefenni is slowly sinking into irreversible ruination. Originally the office of the nearby quarry, its bell signalled the working hours. Its Grade II listing protects it from active demolition but does not shield it from the effects of wind and weather. With some possibility of rescue, one hopes that it will again 'toll the knell of passing day'.

R'alltgoed. The shop/house has collapsed, the rest of the row were to shortly follow (SH780120)

Aberllefenni quarry office, c1980 (SH770908)

In the absence of steam for a steam whistle (itself a Welsh invention), it was commonplace in quarrying to denote time, signal emergencies, or give warnings, by means of a bell at the office. Few can have done so with a more ecclesiastical aura than at the Parciau 'marble' quarry at Penmon, Anglesey. This quarry which in fact produced a high grade limestone, was colloquially known as Penrhyn quarry due to its having supplied much raw material for Penrhyn Castle. The building, a multipurpose office, workshop and possibly barracks was at the quarry site. Stone was carried a few hundred yards to a finishing mill near the jetty at Porth Penmon.

Fortunately not all disused industrial buildings are derelict. The smithy at Rhydau was established to shoe the horses of the 1824 Dinorwig Railway. When less than twenty years later, the Padarn Railway replaced the Dinorwig line, it continued as a general smithy. After many years of decay it has now been re-built as a dwelling.

Office Parciau quarry Anglesey (SH629803)

Old smithy Rhydau (SH566656)

LAVATORIES

A feature of Welsh industrial settlements was the close attention paid to hygiene. Earth closets were sited in gardens or plots, even when these were not adjacent to the houses. This was the case at Blue Cottages, Aberllefenni, which had, some distance away, a communal allotment, divided into plots, each with its own Tŷ Bach.

The arrangements at Abergynolwyn, were more convenient, there the streets of company houses had rail sidings to their back doors. This enabled the night soil to be collected and dispatched for sale as fertiliser, via the Tal-y-llyn Railway.

In some of the remoter and more inhospitably located settlements, with little chance of horticulture, lavatories, often communal, were built over running water. This could mean a trip of several hundred yards across open moor, a daunting prospect on a winter's night, especially if one was to be greeted by a slate seat!

Sometimes in these communal blocks, each household would have its own 'reserved seat' as it were.

Where this was not the case appropriate social conventions developed.

At R'alltgoed for example, the quarry manager had his

Communal lavatory R'alltgoed, near Corris (SH779118)

'Full House' at Rhiwbach (SH744463)

own place of retirement, but the minister had to take his chances with his flock.

The same stream which acted as a sewer, usually also supplied drinking water so great care was taken to ensure that the former was well downstream of the latter. This arrangement would have been admirable had not one village's downstream been the next village's upstream.

Although this did not precisely occur at Treforus the company village of the Gorseddau quarry, the water supply for the manager's appropriately prestigious residence passed through the village as an uncovered conduit. The scope that this offered the more disaffected type of worker beggars imagination!

In spite of being a solidly male environment, slate workers were spared the somewhat al fresco customs of some other industries and, except in the smallest units, lavatories were provided, frequently over the tailraces of water wheels.

Underground, a somewhat relaxed attitude could be taken towards the matter of privacy, since the darkness would protect the modesty of even the most retiring individual.

Oakley Quarry, Blaenau Ffestiniog (SH693470)

Underground at Cambrian Slate Quarry (SJ189378)

ARTEFACTS OF SLATE

Industry can make its mark on the landscape in big ways, such as the huge waste heaps of slate working or the somewhat lesser detritus of mining or manufacture, or on a human level, the villages and towns which it created. It can also leave behind a legacy of roads or railways and perhaps ports.

Besides these and the derelict structures, collapsing earthworks and decaying masonry; small fragments and details can also be reminders of a lost skill or a forgotten activity.

The 'Corris Binocular' is well known. It is a pair of twin experimental borings made by a tunnelling machine at Abercwmeidaw slate quarry in Corris Uchaf during the late 1860s. The machine, possibly a Brunton, would have been powered by a remote engine via a rope drive, and would have cut by a trepanning action, leaving a central core which could be broken up and removed. One fragment of core remains.

Also at Corris, the remarkable strength of the Narrow Vein slate is shown by its use for coalhole covers. Such covers, well under an inch thick, sustain the weight of large vehicles

Core fragment from trepanning machine, Corris Uchaf

Slate coal-hole cover Corris

riding on the pavement to pass in the narrow street.

Again at Corris, the pulpit in the parish church is, possibly uniquely, made of slate. Its brilliant black shine with gold linings is an excellent example of the slate enamelling process, which was pioneered in the area. Interestingly, the electrical switchboards which were among the final products of Braich Goch slate quarry prior to its 1970s closure, were similarly black enamelled.

Pulpit Corris parish church

From the 1850s to well into the 20th century, slate artifacts were offered with baked-on enamel finishes in order to widen slate's decorative appeal and to distance it from a perception of it being a peasant material.

Corris slate was particularly well suited to withstand the thermal stresses of the process and besides the oven at Braich Goch, there was one at the Aberllefenni 'Magnus' factory and at least two others in nearby Machynlleth.

Just as the Corris enamelled pulpit indicates a local industry, so the memorial to 'Dead Boots' near Blaenau Ffestiniog indicates another very different activity.

During WW2, with quarry jobs scarce, an army boot repair factory was established in Blaenau Ffestiniog Market Hall, providing employment for quarrymen too old or unfit for military service. Boots beyond repair were taken to the Crimea pass and burnt.

Long after the factory closed, the mound of ash with its tens of thousands of boot-irons and its millions of nails, known locally as 'Boot Hill' received this memorial.

The gesture was intended to be humorous, but it does record an ephemeral but important activity.

'Dead Boots' at 'Boot Hill', Blaenau Ffestiniog

Dry stonewalling is an excellent means of marking field boundaries since they provide shelter for stock and can offer protection from soil erosion. They are labour intensive but the raw material is free, excellent when people had plenty of time but no money. Not true in the modern world, but fortunately grants and subsidies have enabled the old skills to be maintained.

There are of course circumstances where fencing rather than walling is called for. Traditionally in Gwynedd the denoting of boundaries, the confining of paths and famously the universal fencing of narrow-gauge railways has been by wiring together suitable lengths of discarded slate.

For years it seemed that the lack of quarrying to generate the slate and the ready availability of off-the-shelf materials, had put an end to wired slate... However, recently there are signs that its days are far from over and once again this delightful and traditional form of fencing is making a come back.

There are many other ways in which slate can be used for fencing, as actual sheets to make a solid fence, as posts and rails even, but the use of slate posts to support strained-wire fencing is most unusual and could be unique.

By the mid 19th century cisterns were a standard

Recent slate fencing at Hafod y Llan near Watkin Path to Snowdon

Most unusual slate fencing post, Dolwyddelan

catalogued slate product. They were sold as a kit comprising, five slabs, grooved where appropriate, together with four screwed-end rods to hold them together (after the manner of the flat-pack furniture of one hundred years later).

Cisterns were priced by capacity, either in gallons or cubic feet. A range of sizes of up to 300 gallons or 50 cubic feet were usually listed as standards. Larger sizes and special capacities being available to order.

Huge panels went to make vats for breweries such as Guinness of Dublin, and extremely large examples were made by Penrhyn quarry in the 1900s for Germany.

A furore resulted during WW1 when it was alleged that these were being used to make explosives for the German navy.

These cisterns were a precision product and could only be economically produced in quantity when machines were available to accurately saw, plane and groove them. Prior to this the only way to make a vessel out of slate, or any stone for that matter, had been to chisel it out from a solid slab. Although for

Standard slate cistern in farm use in Cwm Llefenni

Cisterns, or possibly milk cooling pans, probably 18th century (or earlier) near Tremadog

obvious reasons cisterns so produced tended to be of minimum depth, the operation might be justly called 'labour intensive'.

Cold cupboard made of slate near Llanberis

One characteristic of slate, which made it attractive for cisterns, is its high specific heat so that in hot weather it would help to keep contents cool and in winter delay freezing. This property also made slate useful for dairy and larder slabs.

A slate cupboard could, in the 19th century make an excellent refrigerator. If located outdoors in the shade it would have retained the night chill through much of the day. This one being in what had been a quarry supervisor's house, it may well have been an unofficial 'perk'.

Now that refrigerators are universal, it is difficult to realise what a problem the storage of food was only a generation or two ago.

The great mansions traditionally had icehouses, underground chambers where the winter ice could be stored to preserve food and to provide summer drinks and sorbets.

Just occasionally they were found in more modest residences and there are at least two known in the owner/manager's homes of small slate quarries, Hafodlas near Betws-y-coed and at Cefn Gam, on the Mawddach.

At Cefn Gam although the house is ruinous, there are vestiges of a rather nice garden. It is tempting to visualise a hot summer Sunday afternoon with the family enjoying cold cordials on the lawn, some compensation for the hardships of winter in such an isolated and elevated place.

As a handy and versatile vernacular material and often available very cheaply indeed, slate was put to unintended uses. Capt. Erasmus Gower of Castel Malgwyn, Pembrokeshire amalgamated

Ice house Cefn Gam quarry (SH680256)

some Cilgerran slate quarries, in 1874, just when the trade was falling into the doldrums. Pursuing a vigorously realistic policy he heavily advertised surplus slab items at bargain prices. It is almost certain that the various slate slabs around Llwyngwair Manor Holiday Park are Capt. Gower's bargains.

The Llwyngwair slabs were bought in the normal way of trade, but around quarries, apart from the picking up of discards from the tips, it was always possible to obtain slate at little or no charge. Settlement for services, such as cartage, might be made in slate; hence on farms and elsewhere one frequently sees slate put to many uses some commonplace, but some quite improbable. Few could be more bizarre than what is most definitely a 'slate roof' on an outhouse near Llanberis, where slate rafters and purlins support a covering of slate slabs.

Often this use of slate could go much beyond the purely utilitarian. In the slate districts it made an obvious building medium, but its ability to be carved and shaped often resulted in some elaborate and pleasing designs. Even property which

Slate tables at Llwyngwair Manor, Pembrokeshire

Slate slab roof with slate rafters and purlins, near Llanberis

at the time, was built down to a price, can have some delightful detail.

Slate being readily shaped and incised, fostered artistic skills amongst men used to working with it. Such men were due to the vagaries of trade and of weather, often idle. At such times employers might set them to work on cosmetic or ornamental tasks rather than discharge them.

It is possible that this is the origin of the richly decorated but highly utilitarian animal feed bin in the cow house of the home farm of a Gwynedd quarry owner.

This would seem to confirm the saying that the gentry' animals lived better than their tenants, but it must be said that in the 19th century artefacts similarly decorated would often be found in the most exiguous of dwellings

Doorway. Blaenau Ffestiniog

Carved slate cattle food bin Gwynedd

BITS & CURIOS

Fragments of tools or machines can be valuable evidence of past activities and old skills, even the most trifling part can be a clue to methodology and custom.

In a small slate quarry, sawn-ends with circular marks are not a 100% indication that circular saws were used, since it is possible that such ends were brought in as building blocks. The presence of a circular blade is a clincher. Although these blades were used in huge numbers there are surprisingly few to be found.

Much rarer are sand-saw blades. These toothless reciprocating saws cut by the action of wet sand in the saw-cut. They gave a better finish than circular saws, but they were painfully slow.

Acceptable perhaps if power driven, but to use one of the hand-held versions must have been indeed a hard way to earn a living.

Old sandsaw blades making a fence at Dolwyddelan presumably came from Ty'n y Bryn quarry that used these long out-dated saws up to its 1924 closure. It is possible that one of these blades was the last sand-saw blade ever to cut slate in Wales.

The slab to be cut was laid

Circular saw blade Cwt y Bugail quarry (SH734469)

Old sand saw blades Dolwyddelan

flat, with the saw making a long, shallow, horizontal cut. Understandably, if a hand-held saw was being used, the last quarter inch or so was broken off. Slabs and off-cuts with the resulting part-broken edge can still be found.

In Pembrokeshire slate workings, the lack of fast flowing streams to power saws and most units being too small to afford steam engines, meant that most slabs were hand-sawn. Oddly, sand-saws were almost unknown, almost all cutting was done with quite small, coarse-toothed, two handed saws, which would not have looked, out of place in a carpenter's shop. Owing to the short blade length, the slab had to be precariously stood on end.

A few pictures show such saws in use but it is unlikely that any complete example survives. This blade dug up in a garden in Cilgerran during the 1990s, may be unique.

Circular saw blades were discarded when repeated re-sharpening reduced their diameter to a point which made the peripheral speed too low for effective cutting, but not all discarded saws were thrown away. One at the head of the underground 7-6 haulage incline at Braich

Unique (?) remnant of a Pembrokeshire slate saw, Cilgerran

Signal gong, Braich Goch (SH748078)

Goch slate quarry at Corris, enabled a man at the foot to communicate with the winch man at the top.

Underground, there can be other oddities. The only explosive used for slate winning is Black Powder, since high explosive would shatter the rock.

However, development work tunnelling through hard rock, did call for high explosives. Some of the old nitro based high explosives could be sensitive to low temperatures, hence they were carried in hot-water jacketed containers slung on a man's back. An example was found in a now inaccessible chamber of Cwmorthin quarry during the 1980s.

Finds underground can be surprising. The minimum winter temperature in underground workings is around 50°, so how in early 1988 a chamber in Brynglas quarry was frozen so hard, that drips from the roof formed ice 'stalactites'?

The explanation is that to facilitate the installation of a ropeway during re-working in the early 1960s a second entrance was cut, giving a through and in this case, chilling, draught

Before the advent of electricity and of motors cheap enough to provide independent drive to each piece of equipment, mill and factory machines were driven from a central power source by line shafting. This shafting had pulleys to carry the various belt drives. These pulleys were usually of cast iron and of around a foot in diameter.

A magnificent fabricated pulley over three feet across, was in a mill at Penyrorsedd slate quarry, and was part of the unique arrangement whereby two entirely separate mills shared a water-wheel.

At Rhiw Goch slate quarry are two very odd

High-explosive carrier Cwmorthin (SH681459)

Icicles Brynglas quarry (SH732423)

Sheave for temporary ropeway Brynglas

shaped tanks, which were used to store fuel for the oil engine. They are apparently from motor torpedo boats broken up after WW1.

Interestingly this would appear to continue the tradition of using ex-marine items such as winches, donkey engines and possibly boilers. Such trade emphasised the close affinity of Welsh slate workings with the sea.

It is extremely rare to find much in the way of 'heavy metal' at an extractive site, the 'piano' stamp box at Britannia copper mine on the Meinars Track to Snowdon, being a well-known exception.

The rarest items are the cast iron rolls used to crush metallic ores, since they may not even have to be carried to be moved.

Some exist at Cwm Cowarch lead mine at Dinas Mawddwy, because they have rolled into places, extrication from which would call for lifting tackle, which presumably the scrappers did not have.

Remoteness and a less than total clearance have meant that several rolls remain in situ at Cwm Erch copper mine high on the southern flanks of Snowdon.

Large pulley, Penyrorsedd (SH510538)

Rhiw Goch slate quarry ex-marine tank (SJ169453)

Curiously they include a worn pair which it is believed were never used here and which, it is suggested, must have been bought as spares.

On the rocky beach at Rhiw, are fragments of a winch, now much rusted from their diurnal salt-water immersion. It may have accidentally fallen onto the beach during the scrapping-out of one of the several manganese mines which loaded nearby, and thought not worth the effort of retrieving

Pair of crusher rolls Cwm Erch copper mine (SH634531)

Overhead cable conveyor systems were once quite widely used. They took mine waste to tipping grounds and carried metal ores and stone, often for appreciable distances. Since their towers were usually easily felled, very few long survived a mine or quarry's closure.

An exception was the one at Cwm Bychan copper mine near Beddgelert. This mine was a bold but unsuccessful 1920s attempt to re-open an 18th century operation. Had it succeeded its output might have provided some sorely needed revenue for the Welsh Highland Railway.

Astonishingly, in spite of access not being difficult and the fact that it would have

Wreckage of winch on beach at Rhiw (SH243285)

taken a minimum of cutting to dismember the towers, almost every one of them and some of the ancillary equipment survive.

In ancient times indicator flora was used to locate minerals. The presence of plants known to absorb copper compounds for instance would show where to dig for that metal. At Dolfrwynog north of Dolgellau the vegetation was so rich in copper that the turf was cut and burnt in vast open-air grates, the ash being bagged and sold to the Swansea smelters.

Upper terminus & towers Cwm Bychan cableway (SH605476)

Dolfrwynog turf 'mine' grate. (SH747256)

THE FUTURE

In recent years, road improvements have brought further threats to industrial monuments.

In the 1990s such improvements robbed us of much of the historic Chwarel Ddu quarry. Dating from at least the 18th century, it was the oldest in the area and it was the need to take its slate to the river Conwy that caused the picturesque Dolwyddelan-Betws-y-coed road to be built in 1810.

There is now (2002) a threat of further loss of heritage at Blaenau Ffestiniog, with road widening and a scheme to reclaim tips for hardcore. These two proposals will threaten one of the most concentrated areas of industrial remains in northern Wales.

Within it is the site of the original Dinas terminus of the Ffestiniog Railway and its four quarry feeders. On one side of the main line railway, are the formations of the exchange sidings for the Oakeley quarry and on the other, those of the sidings and stockyard for the Llechwedd quarries as well as the Llechwedd

Chwarel Ddu quarry c 1980 (SH876565)

Blaenau Ffestiniog. Main line railway emerges from tunnel, Oakeley exchange sidings to r. Llechwedd sidings, yard and power station to l. Abandoned Ffestiniog Dinas line crosses unseen r to l. Also the abutments and a pillar of the Bont Goch viaduct.

hydroelectric station.

Slate waste already abuts the Dinas engine shed, the last unengulfed vestige of what was a flourishing hamlet and the original terminus of the Ffestiniog Railway.

Dinas engine shed Ffestiniog Railway

It is impossible to retain everything that is old, and futile to try to do so, particularly when to do so would impede legitimate regeneration and reuse. At the same time every relic that is lost diminishes in some degree the total sum of human knowledge. It also robs us of an icon by which we may seek to understand the past, comprehend the present and plan the future.

However when conserving and preserving edifices and artefacts, it must be bourn in mind that these are not mere sticks and stones but are monuments to the people who devised, created and used them.

Thus it is most appropriate that of all the structures and objects at Penyrorsedd quarry, the War Memorial should be singled out for preservation, and re-erection in Nantlle village. It is a reminder of how devastating were the losses particularly in WW1 where Welsh slate men suffered proportionately more deaths than those of any other industry.

Nor should the preservation of skills be neglected, and it is fortunate that museums and other bodies as well as private individuals and groups are reviving and nurturing ancient crafts.

Thanks to them old crafts such as building, weaving, smelting, casting, wood and metalworking, are being actively used and maintained.

Besides the obvious crafts, more esoteric activities are being revived.

It was the custom in slate quarrying and other areas where

Penyrorsedd quarry war memorial re-sited in Nantlle village

gunpowder was used to celebrate great occasions by discharging 'Rock Cannon'.

These were a series of groove-connected holes in a flat rock, filled with gunpowder to provide a cascade of reports. Recently the exact way in which this was done has been researched and, on appropriate occasions, replicated.

Casting at the Welsh Slate Museum, Llanberis

See Rock Cannon of Gwynedd by G R Jones Blaenau Ffestiniog 2002

NOT the 'last active volcano in Meirionnydd', but the Fforwm Tan y Bwlch Historical Research Group celebrating the 50th anniversary of VJ day at Blaenau Ffestiniog in traditional manner.

INDEX TO PICTURES